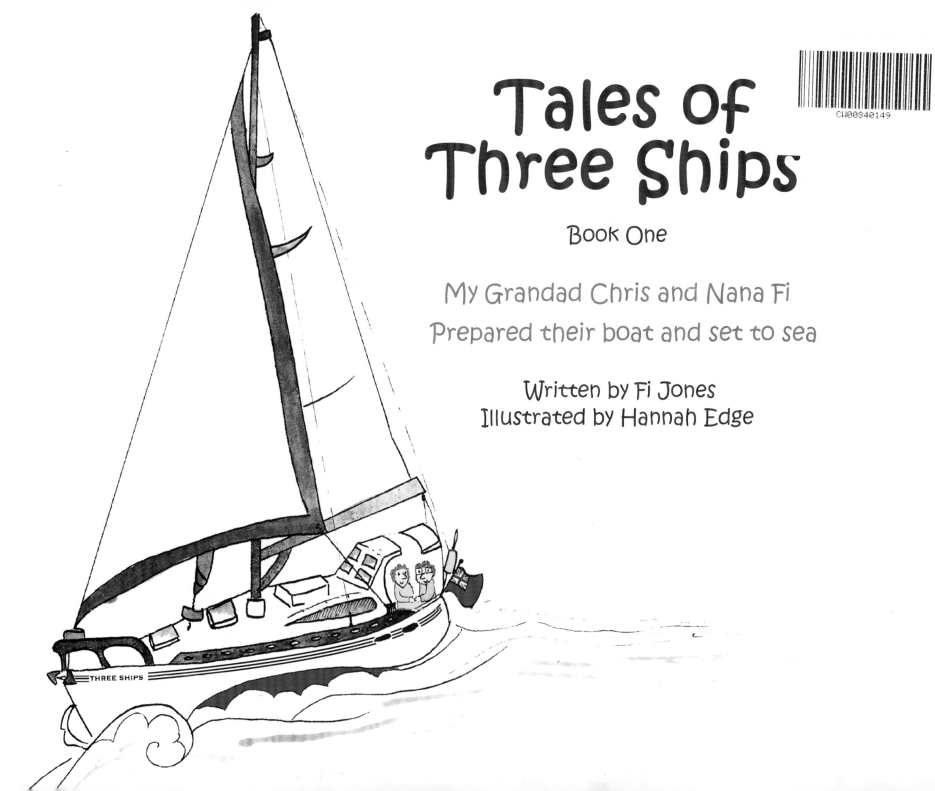

Tales of Three Ships

Book One

My Grandad Chris and Nana Fi
Prepared their boat and set to sea

Written by Fi Jones
Illustrated by Hannah Edge

My Grandad Chris and my Nana Fi
Have a house by a park
right near the sea
They push me on the swings
they let me climb the slide
And help me feed the swans
if I'm lucky with the tide.

THREE SHIPS

ISBN 978-1-9999031-0-7

Printed By Fiona J Jones

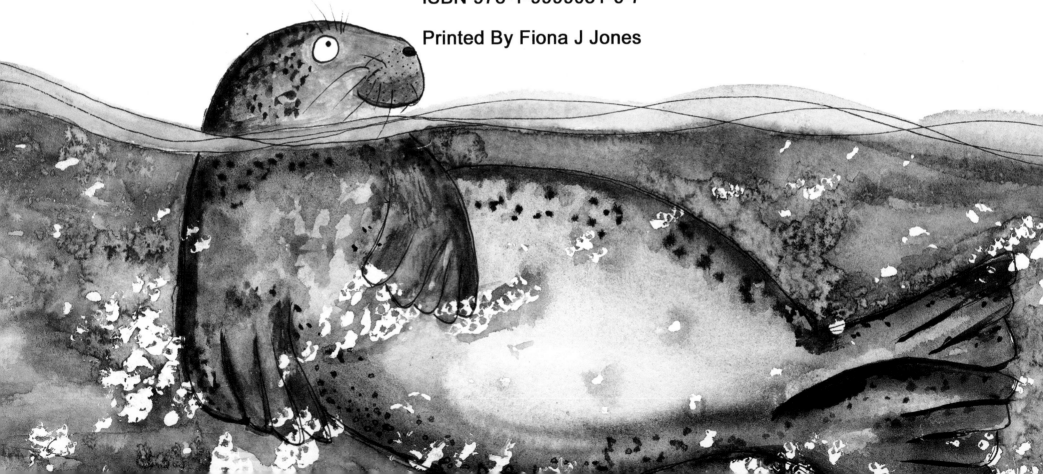

Well that is here in Wales, whenever they are home
But as Mum says **"they have a tendency to roam"**,
For most of the year they lead adventurous lives afloat
Living aboard "Three Ships" which is their sailing boat.

Years ago, before I was born, they made her ready for sea,
But never really told my Mum how long their voyage would be.

Nana Fi squeezed in and packed every type of food and drink...
And Grandad Chris stowed lots of spares and useful bits I think.

They threw a farewell party on
Port Dinorwic Dock
For all their friends and family
right beside the lock.

Next morning, sharp at nine,
to catch the tidal flow
They set off down the
Menai Strait making quite
a show.

Out into the Irish Sea chop
they crossed Caernarfon Bar
With Nana Fi at the wheel they
headed for lands afar,
Grandad Chris went down below
to ponder over the chart,
As navigation
(that's finding the way)
is something of an art!

Grandad Chris manned the halyard
winch up for'ard at the mast
He wound the main sail to the top
and came back to the cockpit fast.
He winched out the head sail
sheeting tight til' it caught the
breeze,
Then with a final look at home
he gave Nana Fi's hand a squeeze.

THREE SHIPS

Nana Fi stopped the engine and still
"Three Ships" picked up speed
A bow wave formed and wake streamed
aft, a perfect sail indeed.

THREE SHIPS

Wake

Bow Wave

Further and further out to sea,
the land became quite small.
Then there was only sea and sky...

and nothing else at all...

When darkness fell they sailed on throughout the starry night.
The morning forecast warned of gales and turned out to be right.

Bravely they reefed the sails
and set wind-vane George to steer.

Still Three Ships sailed happily,
heeled over on her ear.

Three hours up in the cockpit, that's how the watches run...

...Then three hours rest in a roly bunk, it isn't always fun.

Across the Bay of Biscay with a huge four metre swell,
They plotted their progress on the chart
and wrote the log as well.

The wind began to drop and they
changed course for the coast
So Nana Fi prepared a treat of some
lovely cheese on toast.

In readiness for landfall they began
to tidy up and clean.
All the mess and muddle showed what
a rough trip it had been.

Nana Fi raised the Q flag and the Portuguese one too,
On entering a foreign port that's what you have to do.

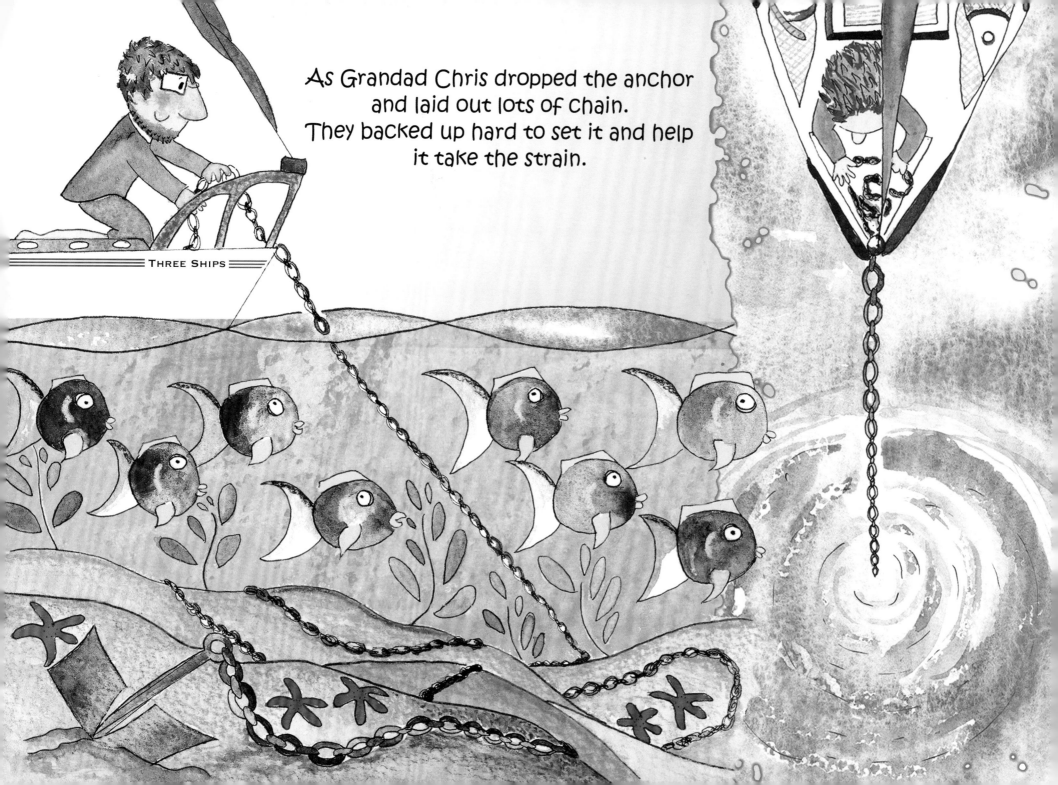

As Grandad Chris dropped the anchor
and laid out lots of chain.
They backed up hard to set it and help
it take the strain.

THREE SHIPS

On land their legs
were wobbly
from all those days
at sea
And customs and
immigration
were about to
close for tea,

CHIEF
CASHIER

They filled out forms,
had passports stamped and
paid fees to the chief cashier...
Then ventured out to
a friendly bar
for a long cold ginger beer.

To see some more
of Portugal Grandad Chris
drove a car inland

Passing corks being made by farmers
growing cork trees in the sand.

festival
de país

suco de
maçã

apple juice

suco de
pera
pear juice

There was a country festival; they found it quite by chance And tasted most unusual foods watching a Portuguese dance.

Deeper into the countryside they drove for many miles
And all the local people greeted them with friendly smiles.
Three wheeled trucks and donkeys carried traders to the local markets
Selling fruit and veg' and chillies on strings from woven wicker baskets.

On to modern Portugal
they reached Lisbon,
the capital city,
The churches, parks
and narrow streets
were really rather pretty.

Then at Europe's most western point,
the cliffs of St Vincent's Cape

They saw a monument to Captain Cook
in a giant compass shape.

Back at port they made "Three Ships" ready again for sea,
Then rowed ashore for coffee and a cake for Nana Fi.

They talked about their options,
should they really head for home?
With all the rest of the World
to cruise surely they had to roam?

That was the beginning of this tale from Nana Fi,
I heard it first in Wales while sat upon her knee.

It was getting late so there we stopped as I tried to hide a yawn, And Grandad Chris tucked me into bed where I dreamed of boats till dawn.

Watch out for the next book in the series and join
Grandad Chris and Nana Fi as they cross oceans and interact
with the wildlife they meet along the way.

For more information check out
www.talesofthreeships.co.uk

Fi and Chris Jones were teaching sailing on their 43' Yacht "Three Ships" when they decided to take a break and set off to cruise further afield. Fourteen years later they sailed her back into their home port of Caernarfon after circumnavigating the globe and having had many adventures along the way.

Illustrator Hannah Edge has known Chris & Fi since she was a child when they raced against her parents at Y Felinheli sailing club. She is also a keen sailor and races a Scorpion dinghy and sometimes crews racing yachts in the Solent.